First published in 2020 by Scholastic Children's Books
Euston House, 24 Eversholt Street, London NW1 1DB
A division of Scholastic Ltd

www.scholastic.co.uk

London – New York – Toronto – Sydney – Auckland – Mexico City – New Delhi – Hong Kong

Text © Wow World Group Limited, 2020
Adapted from the song, "Say Hello to The Sun" by Baby Sensory.

Illustrations by Lindsey Sagar © Scholastic Children's Books, 2020

ISBN 978 070230 335 7
Printed in China

1 2 3 4 5 6 7 8 9 10

Say Hello to the Sun

Written by Dr Lin Day

Illustrated by Lindsey Sagar

Say **hello** to the sun, **shining** down on me,

I **love** the sun,
because the sun **warms** me.

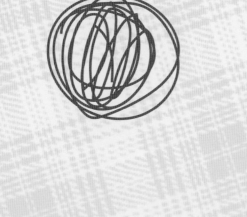

Say hello to the moon,
beaming down on me,

I **love** the moon,
because the moon **guides** me.

Say **hello** to the corn,
growing strong for me,

I **love** the corn, because the corn **feeds** me.

Say **hello** to the stars,
shining down on me.

I **love** the stars,
because the stars **see** me.

Say **hello** to the rain, **falling** down on me.

I **love** the rain, because the rain **cools** me.

Say **hello** to the flowers, **bright** colours for me,

I **love** the flowers,
Because they **gladden** me.

Say **hello**
to my friends,
playing games with me,

I **love** my friends,
Because my friends **love** me,

How to use this book

Cuddle up with your baby and read the words, do the signs and talk about the pictures, elements and colours.

Download the song and sing along with your baby – you can do the signs too!

Read this book on a regular basis. Take note of the following from your baby:

· Look out for your baby's expressions; are they recognising the images?

· Notice what they do when you sing; has your baby started to imitate your signs?

· Does your baby stop what they are doing when you turn on the music? Do they get excited? Mesmerised?

· Does your baby settle to the sound of the song?

Sun

Make a `C` shape with your whole hand above your head.

Moon

Make a `C` shape with your forefinger and thumb above your head.

Corn

Push the fingers of one hand through the other hand to represent a shoot pushing its way through the soil.

Stars

Hold your hands up in front of you and wiggle your fingers.

Rain

Wriggle the fingers of both hands downwards to represent rain falling.

Flowers

Pinch your fingers together and bring them to your nose.

Friends

Hook the fingers of both hands together and move them up and down.

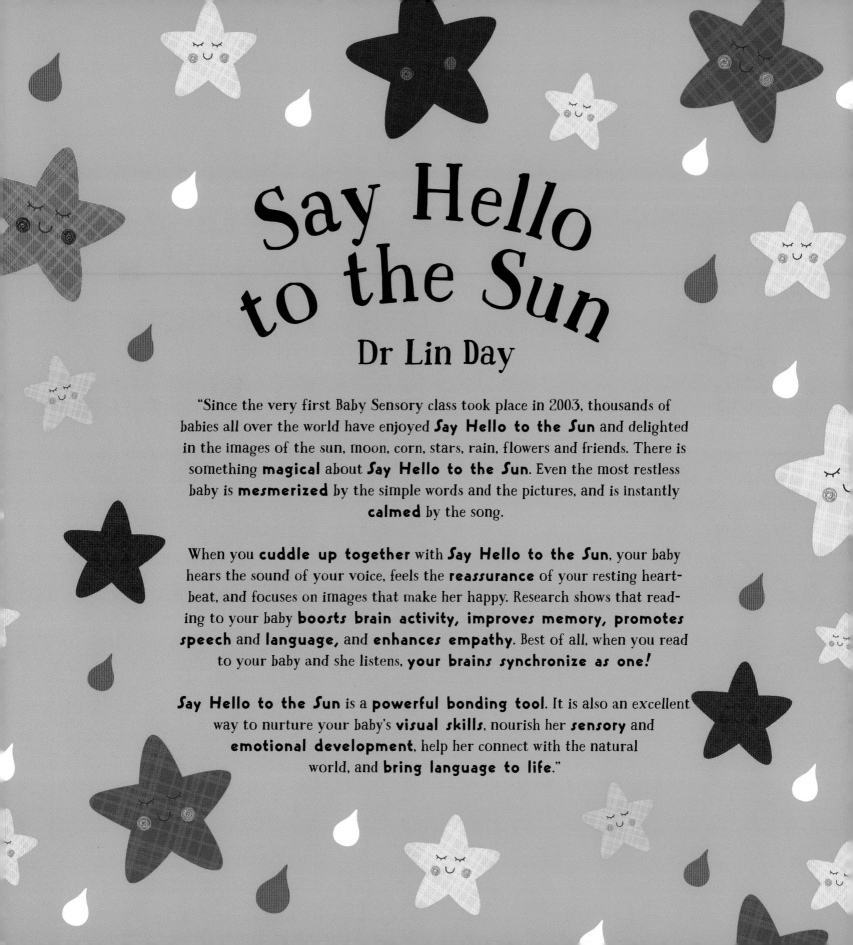

Say Hello to the Sun

Dr Lin Day

"Since the very first Baby Sensory class took place in 2003, thousands of babies all over the world have enjoyed **Say Hello to the Sun** and delighted in the images of the sun, moon, corn, stars, rain, flowers and friends. There is something **magical** about **Say Hello to the Sun**. Even the most restless baby is **mesmerized** by the simple words and the pictures, and is instantly **calmed** by the song.

When you **cuddle up together** with **Say Hello to the Sun**, your baby hears the sound of your voice, feels the **reassurance** of your resting heartbeat, and focuses on images that make her happy. Research shows that reading to your baby **boosts brain activity, improves memory, promotes speech** and **language,** and **enhances empathy**. Best of all, when you read to your baby and she listens, **your brains synchronize as one!**

Say Hello to the Sun is a **powerful bonding tool**. It is also an excellent way to nurture your baby's **visual skills**, nourish her **sensory** and **emotional development**, help her connect with the natural world, and **bring language to life.**"